Andrew Brodie Basics

LET'S DO MENTAL MATHS

FOR AGES 10-11

with over **100** reward stickers

- Over 800 practice questions
- Regular progress tests
- Extra tips and brain booster questions

First published 2013 by Bloomsbury Publishing plc
50 Bedford Square, London, WC1B 3DP
www.bloomsbury.com

ISBN 978-1-4081-8342-7

Copyright © 2013 Bloomsbury Publishing plc
Written by Andrew Brodie
Design by Marcus Duck
Cover and inside illustrations of Digit the Dog and Andrew Brodie © Nikalas Catlow

10 9 8 7 6 5 4 3 2

A CIP record for this publication is available from the British Library.

Printed in China by Leo Paper Products

This book is produced using paper that is made from wood grown in managed, sustainable forests. It is natural, renewable and recyclable. The logging and manufacturing processes conform to the environmental regulations of the country of origin.

To see our full range of titles visit www.bloo

BLOOMSBUR

Notes for parents

What's in this book

This is the sixth book in an exciting new series of *Andrew Brodie Basics: Let's Do Mental Maths* books. Each book contains more than 800 mental maths questions specially devised to boost children's confidence by providing plenty of practice in all the key aspects of the National Curriculum:

- Number and place value
- Addition and subtraction
- Multiplication and division
- Fractions
- Measures
- Geometry

The structure of each test follows the same pattern but the questions become gradually more difficult as the book progresses. You will notice that some questions are repeated to help your child learn and then revise vital facts such as identifying shapes: squares, triangles, rectangles and circles. Taking the time to discuss the questions with your child and helping to explain anything they find difficult will produce the best results. Answers to all the questions are provided at the back of the book.

How you can help

To begin with your child might find the tests quite tricky but as they work their way through the book and become more familiar with the different types of question their confidence will grow. At the end of every five tests there is a Progress Test which will help you and your child to review some of the key concepts and will also highlight anything they haven't understood so far. Always provide lots of encouragement and explain that they should learn from their mistakes rather than be disheartened.

Children gain confidence by learning facts that they can use in their work at school. Help your child by displaying posters on their bedroom wall, showing facts such as the times tables, days of the week and months of the year. Talk about these facts with your child and discuss the number of days in each month. You could use this rhyme to help them r

Thirty days has September,
April, June and November.
All the rest have thirty-one,
Except for February alone,
Which has twenty-eight days clear
And twenty-nine in each leap year.

Some children find difficulty with the concept of fractions so this is something you can help them with quite easily. Explain that the circle below is cut into eight pieces so we are dealing with eighths; seven of these are shaded so the fraction shaded is seven eighths:

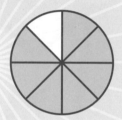

Digit the Dog and Brain Boosters

Look out for useful tips from Digit the Dog who provides little snippets of mathematical information that your child needs to know or quick questions to get them thinking!

Brodie's Brain Boosters feature short mathematical problems, which can be solved by working logically. Some of these may look very straightforward but the thinking processes that your child will need to apply are important skills to practise, ready for more challenging work later. Understanding the wording of questions is a crucial aspect of problem solving so ensure that your child reads each question carefully – give some help with the vocabulary if necessary.

With lots of practice and encouragement your child will see their score improve day by day!

TEST 1

1   4 x 4 + 6 =

2   Add 60 to 140.

3   230 – 48 =

4   What is the difference between 1,000 and 260?

5   Double 45 =

6   6 x 8 + 7 =

7   What is 84 shared between 4?

8   89 ÷ 10 =

9   Write < or >. 75   57

10   Round 183 to the nearest ten.

11   What is the next number in this sequence? 46, 50, 54, 58, …

12   Simplify the fraction $\frac{4}{8}$

13   Write this fraction as a decimal $\frac{1}{4}$

14   10% of 80 =

15 $a + 6 = 8$ $a =$

16 $\frac{1}{2}$ hour =   minutes

17   What is the area of the rectangle?

6cm

4cm

18   1m – 62cm =

19   What size is the missing angle?

142°

20   Give the mean for the following data: 16 9 5

Brodie's Brain Booster

I think of a number. I add 28 then multiply by 5. The answer is 200. What number did I first think of?

3

TEST 2

Digit says...

Remember, to find the mean add the numbers together then divide by the number of numbers! So in question 20 you have to divide by 3.

1 $6 \times 4 + 7 =$

2 Add 80 to 230

3 $370 - 99 =$

4 What is the difference between 1,000 and 350?

5 Double 65 =

6 $7 \times 8 + 6 =$

7 What is 96 shared between 4?

8 $93 \div 10 =$

9 Write < or >. 89   98

10 Round 216 to the nearest ten.

11 What is the next number in this sequence? 81, 85, 89, 93, ...

12 Simplify the fraction $\frac{6}{12}$

13 Write this fraction as a decimal $\frac{1}{2}$

14 10% of 240 =

15 $a + 7 = 10$ $a =$

16 $\frac{1}{4}$ hour =   minutes

17 What is the area of the rectangle?

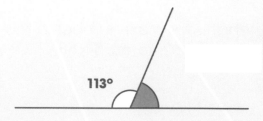

6cm

3cm

18 1m – 38cm =

19 What size is the missing angle?

113°

20 Give the mean for the following data: 23   18   19

4

TEST 3

1 $3 \times 4 + 9 =$

2 Add 90 to 560

3 $720 - 87 =$

4 What is the difference between 1,000 and 780?

5 Double 98 =

6 $5 \times 8 + 9 =$

7 What is 72 shared between 4?

8 $47 \div 10 =$

9 Write < or >. 67 _____ 76

10 Round 472 to the nearest ten.

11 What is the next number in this sequence? 75, 79, 83, 87, …

12 Simplify the fraction $\frac{4}{12}$

13 Write this fraction as a decimal $\frac{3}{4}$

14 10% of 170 =

15 $a + 9 = 15$ $a =$

16 $\frac{3}{4}$ hour = _____ minutes

17 What is the area of the rectangle?

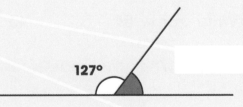

2cm | 6cm

18 1m − 46cm =

19 What size is the missing angle?

127°

20 Give the mean for the following data: 32 24 16

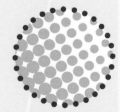

Brodie's Brain Booster

I think of a number.
I divide by 3. The answer is
49. What number did
I first think of?

5

TEST 4

1 $8 \times 4 + 5 =$

2 Add 80 to 330.

3 $910 - 59 =$

4 What is the difference between 1,000 and 590?

5 Double 75 =

6 $8 \times 8 + 7 =$

7 What is 92 shared between 4?

8 $68 \div 10 =$

9 Write < or >. 54   45

10 Round 476 to the nearest ten.

11 What is the next number in this sequence? 86, 90, 94, 98, …

12 Simplify the fraction $\frac{4}{16}$

13 Write this fraction as a decimal $\frac{3}{10}$

14 10% of 530 =

15 $a + 4 = 20$ $a =$

16 $\frac{1}{4}$ hour =   minutes

17 What is the area of the rectangle?

5cm

4cm

18 $1m - 59cm =$

19 What size is the missing angle?

136°

20 Give the mean for the following data: 29 37 24

Digit says...

A parallelogram is quite like a rectangle but its corners are not right angles. I am a genius dog!

TEST 5

1 7 x 4 + 8 =

2 Add 70 to 420.

3 840 – 67 =

4 What is the difference between 1,000 and 680?

5 Double 95 =

6 4 x 8 + 12 =

7 What is 76 shared between 4?

8 83 ÷ 10 =

9 Write < or >. 73 _____ 37

10 Round 386 to the nearest ten.

11 What is the next number in this sequence? 63, 67, 71, 75, …

12 Simplify the fraction $\frac{4}{20}$

13 Write this fraction as a decimal $\frac{7}{10}$

Brodie's Brain Booster

I think of a number. I multiply by 10. The answer is 2,000,000. What number did I think of?

14 10% of 680 =

15 $a + 3 = 16$ $a =$

16 $\frac{1}{2}$ hour = _____ minutes

17 What is the area of the rectangle?

7cm

4cm

18 1m – 28cm =

19 What size is the missing angle?

154°

20 Give the mean for the following data: 25 34 16

7

Addition, subtraction, multiplication and division

1 $9 \times 4 + 6 =$

2 Add 90 to 750.

3 $550 - 88 =$

4 What is the difference between 1,000 and 730?

5 Double 55 =

6 $9 \times 8 + 6 =$

7 What is 68 shared between 4?

8 $56 \div 10 =$

Number, place value and rounding

9 Write < or >. 68 _____ 86

10 Round 887 to the nearest ten.

11 What is the next number in this sequence? 57, 61, 65, 69, ...

Fractions, decimals and percentages

12 Simplify the fraction $\frac{6}{8}$

13 Write this fraction as a decimal $\frac{9}{10}$

14 10% of 760 =

Algebra

15 $a + 5 = 12$ $a =$

Measurement

16 $\frac{3}{4}$ hour = _____ minutes

17 What is the area of the rectangle?

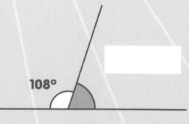

7cm

3cm

18 $1m - 81cm =$

19 What size is the missing angle?

108°

Data

20 Give the mean for the following data: 28 36 23

Score chart

Test	1	2	3	4	5	Progress
Score						

TEST 6

Score:

1   3 x 6 + 5 =

2   Add 139 to 480.

3   340 – 59 =

4   What is the difference between 1,000 and 379?

5   4.6 x 10 =

6   What is the product of 8 and 9?

7   56 ÷ 7 =

8   Half of 210 =

9   Write < or >.   1,069   1,096

10   Round 565 to the nearest ten.

11   What is the next number in this sequence? 56, 62, 68, 74, …

12   Simplify the fraction $\frac{9}{12}$

13   Write this decimal as a fraction 0.5

14   20% of 90 =

15   9 – a = 3   a =

16 $\frac{1}{6}$ hour =   minutes

17   What is the area of the rectangle?

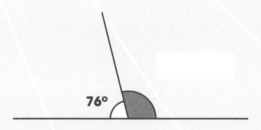

4cm

2.5cm

18   1km – 389m =

19   What size is the missing angle?

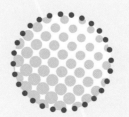

76°

20   Give the mean for the following data: 12   10   7   11

Digit says...

Did you know that a rhombus has 4 equal sides but its corners are not right angles? What a clever dog I am!

1 7 x 6 + 8 =

2 Add 163 to 580

3 520 – 72 =

4 What is the difference between 1,000 and 555?

5 3.6 x 10 =

6 What is the product of 5 and 9?

7 21 ÷ 7 =

8 Half of 410 =

9 Write < or >. 1,118   1,181

10 Round 425 to the nearest ten.

11 What is the next number in this sequence? 71, 77, 83, 89, …

12 Simplify the fraction $\frac{12}{16}$

13 Write this decimal as a fraction 0.25

14 20% of 70 =

15 12 – a = 5   a =

16 $\frac{1}{3}$ hour =   minutes

17 What is the area of the rectangle?

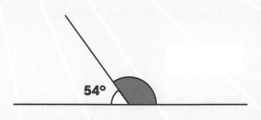

5cm

2.5cm

18 1km – 624m =

19 What size is the missing angle?

54°

20 Give the mean for the following data: 14 17 15 14

Brodie's Brain Booster

I divide by 10. The answer is 4.3. What number did I first think of?

TEST 8

1 9 x 6 + 4 =

2 Add 175 to 690

3 610 – 88 =

4 What is the difference between 1,000 and 682?

5 5.7 x 10 =

6 What is the product of 4 and 9?

7 35 ÷ 7 =

8 Half of 610 =

9 Write < or >. 1,745   1,547

10 Round 635 to the nearest ten.

11 What is the next number in this sequence? 69, 75, 81, 87,

12 Simplify the fraction $\frac{10}{15}$

13 Write this decimal as a fraction 0.75

Digit says...

A trapezium is a quadrilateral, which means it has 4 sides. Told you – I know my shapes!

14 20% of 50 =

15 10 - a = 6   a =

16 $\frac{1}{10}$ hour =   minutes

17 What is the area of the rectangle?

6cm
2.5cm

18 1km – 579m =

19 What size is the missing angle?

83°

20 Give the mean for the following data:
21 18 23 22

Score:

In a Fibonacci sequence each term is made from the sum of the previous two terms. What is the next term in this Fibonacci sequence: 1, 1, 2, 3, …?

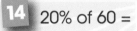

1 6 x 6 + 7 =

2 Add 182 to 720.

3 930 – 94 =

4 What is the difference between 1,000 and 703?

5 2.8 x 10 =

6 What is the product of 7 and 9?

7 42 ÷ 7 =

8 Half of 330 =

9 Write < or >. 1,669 _____ 1,966

10 Round 975 to the nearest ten.

11 What is the next number in this sequence? 81, 87, 93, 99, …

12 Simplify the fraction $\frac{12}{18}$

13 Write this decimal as a fraction 0.9

14 20% of 60 =

15 8 – a = 7   a =

16 $\frac{1}{12}$ hour = _____ minutes

17 What is the area of the rectangle?

8cm

2.5cm

18 1km – 407m =

19 What size is the missing angle?

45°

20 Give the mean for the following data: 16 17 18 9

TEST 10

1 $8 \times 6 + 9 =$

2 Add 159 to 390.

3 $850 - 87 =$

4 What is the difference between 1,000 and 499?

5 $8.9 \times 10 =$

6 What is the product of 6 and 9?

7 $49 \div 7 =$

8 Half of 430 =

9 Write < or >. 1,824   1,842

10 Round 865 to the nearest ten.

11 What is the next number in this sequence? 76, 82, 88, 94, …

12 Simplify the fraction $\frac{20}{25}$

13 Write this decimal as a fraction 0.7

14 20% of 80 =

15 $7 - a = 4$ $a =$

16 $\frac{1}{5}$ hour =   minutes

17 What is the area of the rectangle?

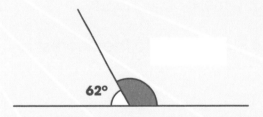

6cm

3.5cm

18 $1km - 708m =$

19 What size is the missing angle?

62°

20 Give the mean for the following data:
14 15 16 15

Digit says...

A trapezium is a quadrilateral with two opposite sides that are parallel, but two opposite sides that are not parallel. Cats know nothing!

13

Addition, subtraction, multiplication and division

1 $4 \times 6 + 8 =$

2 Add 184 to 640.

3 $730 - 64 =$

4 What is the difference between 1,000 and 717?

5 $9.3 \times 10 =$

6 What is the product of 11 and 9?

7 $84 \div 7 =$

8 Half of 630 =

Number, place value and rounding

9 Write < or >. 1,550 [ ] 1,505

10 Round 755 to the nearest ten.

11 What is the next number in this sequence? 79, 85, 91, 97, …

Fractions, decimals and percentages

12 Simplify the fraction $\frac{20}{30}$

13 Write this decimal as a fraction 0.3

14 20% of 75 =

Algebra

15 $11 - a = 8$ $a =$

Measurement

16 $\frac{5}{6}$ hour = [ ] minutes

17 What is the area of the rectangle?

6cm

4.5cm

18 1km – 511m =

19 What size is the missing angle?

57°

Data

20 Give the mean for the following data: 34 11 33 22

Score chart

Test	6	7	8	9	10	Progress
Score						

14

Score:

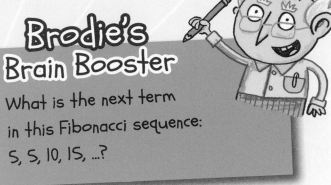

What is the next term in this Fibonacci sequence: 5, 5, 10, 15, ...?

1 5 x 7 + 8 =

2 2,150 plus 1,350 =

3 500 subtract 319 =

4 If I buy some sweets for 26p and 32p what is my change from £1?

5 6 squared =

6 8 x 9 – 6 =

7 Share 850 between 2.

8 230 ÷ 100 =

9 Write < or >. 12,416   12,146

10 Round 1,039 to the nearest ten.

11 What is the next number in this sequence? 82, 78, 74, 70, …

12 $\frac{1}{2}$ x 66 =

13 0.4 x 6 =

14 25% of 120 =

15 5 + a = 8   a =

16 $1\frac{1}{2}$ hours =   minutes

17 What is the area of the rectangle?

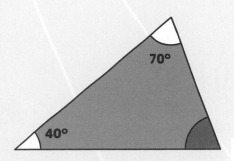

5cm

3.2cm

18 1l – 488ml =

19 What size is the missing angle?

70°

40°

20 Give the mean for the following data: 13 8 15 6

TEST 12

1   4 x 7 + 9 =

2   4,650 plus 1,250 =

3   500 subtract 165 =

4   If I spend 47p and 11p on dog treats what is my change from £1?

5   4 squared =

6   3 x 9 – 8 =

7   Share 650 between 2.

8   470 ÷ 100 =

9   Write < or >. 14,628   14,862

10   Round 3,216 to the nearest ten.

11   What is the next number in this sequence? 104, 98, 92, 86, …

12 $\frac{1}{2}$ x 84 =

13   0.5 x 7 =

14   25% of 200 =

15   8 + a = 12   a =

16 $1\frac{1}{4}$ hours =   minutes

17   What is the area of the rectangle?

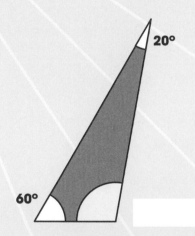

3.2cm

2cm

18   1l – 729ml =

19   What size is the missing angle?

20°

60°

20   Give the mean for the following data: 27 26 18 11

Digit says...

A parallelogram is a quadrilateral. Both pairs of opposite sides are parallel. Try asking a cat to explain that!

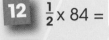

1. 6 x 7 + 5 =

2. 5,350 plus 1,550 =

3. 500 subtract 292 =

4. If I spend 51p and 32p on cat treats what is my change from £1?

5. 5 squared =

6. 4 x 9 – 7 =

7. Share 450 between 2.

8. 810 ÷ 100 =

9. Write < or >. 15,973 ___ 15,793

10. Round 4,151 to the nearest ten.

11. What is the next number in this sequence? 74, 68, 62, 56, …

12. $\frac{1}{2}$ x 68 =

13. 0.6 x 3 =

14. 25% of 280 =

15. 4 + a = 15   a =

16. $1\frac{3}{4}$ hours = ___ minutes

17. What is the area of the rectangle?

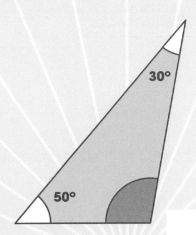
5cm
2.4cm

18. 1l – 804ml =

19. What size is the missing angle?

30°

50°

20. Give the mean for the following data: 21 14 25 18

Brodie's Brain Booster

How much money is $\frac{1}{4}$ of £50?

1   8 x 7 + 6 =

2   6,450 plus 1,550 =

3   500 subtract 388 =

4   If I spend 46p and 24p on dog food what is my change from £1 when?

5   7 squared =

6   5 x 9 – 8 =

7   Share 250 between 2.

8   690 ÷ 100 =

9   Write < or >.   17,552   17,525

10   Round 6,003 to the nearest ten.

11   What is the next number in this sequence? 61, 55, 49, 43, …

12 $\frac{1}{2}$ x 88 =

13   0.7 x 6 =

14   25% of 360 =

15   3 + a = 11   a =

16 $2\frac{1}{2}$ hours =   minutes

17   What is the area of the rectangle?

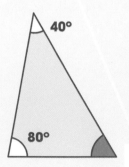

6cm

1.8cm

18   1l – 639ml =

19   What size is the missing angle?

40°

80°

20   Give the mean for the following data: 19 25 13 13

Score:

1 9 x 7 + 4 =

2 3,250 plus 1,750 =

3 500 subtract 178 =

4 If I spend 38p and 23p on cat food what is my change from £1?

5 8 squared =

6 6 x 9 – 7 =

7 Share 350 between 2.

8 520 ÷ 100 =

9 Write < or >. 16,245   16,542

10 Round 4,107 to the nearest ten.

11 What is the next number in this sequence? 93, 87, 81, 75, ...

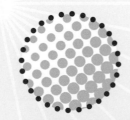

12 $\frac{1}{2}$ x 48 =

13 0.3 x 8 =

14 25% of 480 =

15 6 + a = 13   a =

16 $2\frac{1}{4}$ hours =   minutes

17 What is the area of the rectangle?

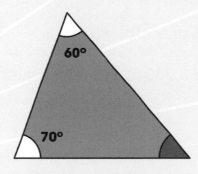

4cm

3.2cm

18 1l – 237ml =

19 What size is the missing angle?

60°

70°

20 Give the mean for the following data: 11 19 24 20

Brodie's Brain Booster

How much money is $\frac{3}{4}$ of £50?

Addition, subtraction, multiplication and division

1 7 x 7 + 8 =

2 4,450 plus 1,250 =

3 500 subtract 263 =

4 If I spend 49p and 35p on toys what is my change from £1?

5 9 squared =

6 7 x 9 – 5 =

7 Share 750 between 2.

8 770 ÷ 100 =

Number, place value and rounding

9 Write < or >. 18,368 [ ] 18,683

10 Round 8,233 to the nearest ten.

11 What is the next number in this sequence? 112, 106, 100, 94, …

Fractions, decimals and percentages

12 $\frac{1}{4}$ x 96 =

13 0.9 x 5 =

14 25% of 720 =

Algebra

15 7 + a = 15   a =

Measurement

16 $2\frac{3}{4}$ hours = [ ] minutes

17 What is the area of the rectangle?

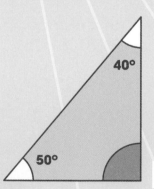

6cm

3.2cm

18 1l – 148ml =

19 What size is the missing angle?

40°

50°

Data

20 Give the mean for the following data: 21 22 23 24

Score chart

Test	11	12	13	14	15	Progress
Score						

Score:

Digit says...

The perimeter of a shape is the distance all the way round the edges. Our daft cat sometimes walks all the way along the top of the perimeter fence rather than across the garden!

1 What is the total of 1,400 and 800?

2 274 + 136 =

3 Decrease 1,460 by 350

4 5,000 take away 2,450 =

5 2 cubed =

6 9 x 4 – 16 =

7 167 ÷ 10 =

8 What is the remainder when 25 is divided by 8?

9 Write < or >. 23,519   32,519

10 Round 2,735 to the nearest hundred.

11 What is the next number in this sequence? 91, 88, 85, 82, ...

12 $\frac{1}{4}$ x 96 =

13 Write $\frac{42}{100}$ as a decimal

14 5% of 60 =

15 a – 6 = 5   a =

16 A half-hour television programme starts at 3.45pm. At what time does it finish?

17 What is the perimeter of the square?

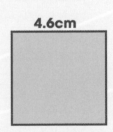

4.6cm

18 10km – 7400m =

19 What size is the missing angle?

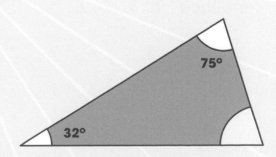

75°

32°

20 Give the mean for the following data:
14 9 8 6

Score:

Brodie's Brain Booster

How much money is $\frac{1}{8}$ of £50?

1 What is the total of 1,600 and 700?

2 329 + 282 =

3 Decrease 1,890 by 420.

4 5,000 take away 1,450 =

5 3 cubed =

6 6 x 4 – 12 =

7 239 ÷ 10 =

8 What is the remainder when 47 is divided by 8?

9 Write < or >. 46,324 ____ 64,234

10 Round 5,142 to the nearest hundred.

11 What is the next number in this sequence? 90, 87, 84, 81, …

12 $\frac{1}{4}$ x 48 =

13 Write $\frac{57}{100}$ as a decimal

14 5% of 80 =

15 a – 7 = 4   a =

16 A half-hour television programme starts at 6.25pm. What time does it finish?

17 What is the perimeter of the square?

3.2cm

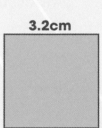

18 10km – 3600m =

19 What size is the missing angle?

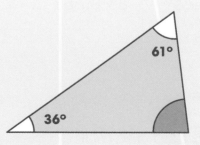

61°

36°

20 Give the mean for the following data: 6 7 8 8

TEST 18

1 What is the total of 1,500 and 900?

2 475 + 169 =

3 Decrease 1,670 by 480.

4 5,000 take away 3,650 =

5 4 cubed =

6 7 x 4 – 14 =

7 358 ÷ 10 =

8 What is the remainder when 34 is divided by 8?

9 Write < or >.   54,003   45,300

10 Round 7,899 to the nearest hundred.

11 What is the next number in this sequence? 72, 69, 66, 63, …

12 $\frac{1}{4}$ x 72 =

13 Write $\frac{93}{100}$ as a decimal

14 5% of 120 =

15 a – 2 = 3   a =

16 A half-hour television programme starts at 7.35pm. What time does it finish?

17 What is the perimeter of the square?

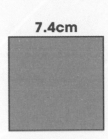

7.4cm

18 10km – 7400m =

19 What size is the missing angle?

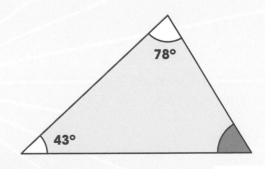

78°

43°

20 Give the mean for the following data: 4 5 6 6

Digit says…

Remember that the perimeter of a circle is called the circumference. For a dog, my vocabulary is pretty amazing!

23

Score:

1 What is the total of 1,800 and 800?

2 386 + 257 =

3 Decrease 1,820 by 550.

4 5,000 take away 2,380 =

5 2 cubed =

6 5 x 4 – 20 =

7 924 ÷ 10 =

8 What is the remainder when 59 is divided by 8?

9 Write < or >. 87,265 □ 78,652

10 Round 6,349 to the nearest hundred.

11 What is the next number in this sequence? 62, 59, 56, 53, …

Brodie's Brain Booster

16 dogs share 144 small dog biscuits. How many do they have each? And what if I eat 143 of them?!

12 $\frac{1}{4}$ x 68 =

13 Write $\frac{69}{100}$ as a decimal

14 5% of 200 =

15 a – 3 = 10   a =

16 A half-hour television programme starts at 6.42pm. What time does it finish?

17 What is the perimeter of the square?

5.9cm

18 10km – 6,800m =

19 What size is the missing angle?

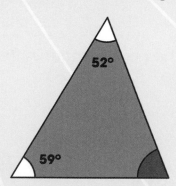

20 Give the mean for the following data: 5 7 9 12

Score: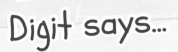

1 What is the total of 1,900 and 300?

2 567 + 234 =

3 Decrease 4,780 by 490.

4 5,000 take away 1,910 =

5 3 cubed =

6 8 x 4 - 14 =

7 706 ÷ 10 =

8 What is the remainder when 67 is divided by 8?

9 Write < or >. 63,738 ____ 36,837

10 Round 3,550 to the nearest hundred.

11 What is the next number in this sequence? 45, 42, 39, 36, …

12 $\frac{1}{4}$ x 84 =

13 Write $\frac{38}{100}$ as a decimal

14 5% of 240 =

15 a – 4 = 9   a =

16 A half-hour television programme starts at 5.40pm. At what time does it finish?

17 What is the perimeter of the square?

2.8cm

18 10km – 7,900m =

19 What size is the missing angle?

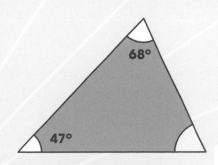

68°

47°

20 Give the mean for the following data: 6 8 10 5

Addition, subtraction, multiplication and division

1 What is the total of 1,400 and 700?

2 682 + 247 =

3 Decrease 5,630 by 460.

4 5,000 take away 2,570 =

5 4 cubed =

6 12 x 4 – 18 =

7 118 ÷ 10 =

8 What is the remainder when 100 is divided by 8?

Number, place value and rounding

9 Write < or >. 38,065 _____ 83,056

10 Round 4,993 to the nearest hundred.

11 What is the next number in this sequence? 111, 108, 105, 102, …

Fractions, decimals and percentages

12 $\frac{1}{4}$ x 92 =

13 Write $\frac{77}{100}$ as a decimal

14 5% of 560 =

Algebra

15 a – 8 = 12   a =

Measurement

16 A half-hour television programme starts at 4.55pm. At what time does it finish?

17 What is the perimeter of the square?

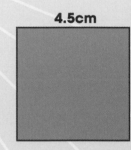
4.5cm

18 10km – 8,300m =

19 What size is the missing angle?

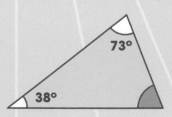
73°
38°

Data

20 Give the mean for the following data: 8 11 14 8

Score:

1 10,250 + 4,350 =

2 I think of a number. I add 42 then subtract 16. The answer is 70. What number did I think of?

3 Add 1,260 to 3,800.

4 10,000 minus 2,600 =

5 The square of 7 =

6 Which of these numbers is a factor of 48? 5 6 10 14

7 2,400 ÷ 3 =

8 Half of 5,000 =

9 Write < or >. 168,594   186,954

10 Round 14,600 to the nearest thousand.

11 What is the next number in this sequence? 500, 475, 450, 425, …

12 $\frac{3}{4}$ x 48 =

13 Write 0.69 as a fraction.

14 40% of 70 =

15 3 x a = 12   a =

16 If 2nd June was a Sunday, what day was 30th May?

17 What is the perimeter of the rectangle?

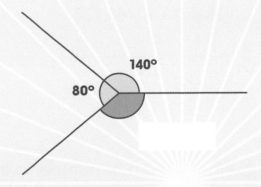

5.9cm

3.2cm

18 10km – 1,480m =

19 What size is the missing angle?

140°

80°

20 Give the mean for the following data: 9 11 5 6

Brodie's Brain Booster

Over the course of 1 week 3 dogs share equally a 4.5kg bag of dog food. How many grams of dog food does each dog have?

27

Score:

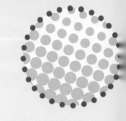

1 10,580 + 6,120 =

2 I think of a number. I add 59 then subtract 23. The answer is 50. What number did I first think of?

3 Add 1,470 to 5,200.

4 10,000 minus 3,700 =

5 The square of 5 =

6 Which of these numbers is a factor of 52? 7 11 13 17

7 1,800 ÷ 3 =

8 Half of 7,000 =

9 Write < or >. 743,225   473,522

10 Round 23,200 to the nearest thousand.

11 What is the next number in this sequence? 600, 580, 560, 540, …

12 $\frac{3}{4}$ x 24 =

13 Write 0.71 as a fraction.

14 30% of 80 =

15 2 x a = 18   a =

16 If 2nd September was a Monday, what day was 30th August?

17 What is the perimeter of the rectangle?

5.9cm

2.9cm

18 10km – 3,260m =

19 What size is the missing angle?

210°

30°

20 Give the mean for the following data: 7 8 9 11

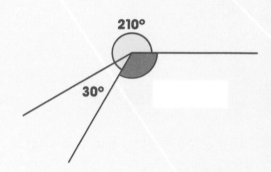

Digit says...

1,000 grams are equal to 1 kilogram and 1,000 kilograms are equal to 1 tonne. I'm still thinking of dog biscuits.

TEST 23

1 10,620 + 7,180 =

2 I think of a number. I add 68 then subtract 31. The answer is 60. What number did I think of?

3 Add 1,390 to 4,700.

4 10,000 minus 4,600 =

5 The square of 4 =

6 Which of these numbers is a factor of 46? 23 24 25 26

7 2,700 ÷ 3 =

8 Half of 9,000 =

9 Write < or >. 567,634   675,643

10 Round 37,900 to the nearest thousand.

11 What is the next number in this sequence? 210, 180, 150, 120, …

12 $\frac{3}{4}$ × 60 =

13 Write 0.83 as a fraction.

Brodie's Brain Booster

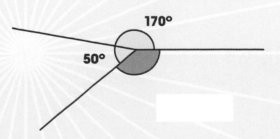

Digit drinks $2\frac{1}{2}$ litres of water every day. How many millilitres of water does he drink in a week?

14 70% of 60 =

15 4 x a = 32   a =

16 If 2nd December was a Thursday, what day was 30th November?

17 What is the perimeter of the rectangle?

6.2cm

4.1cm

18 10km – 8,470m =

19 What size is the missing angle?

170°

50°

20 Give the mean for the following data: 9 10 13 11

Score:

Digit says...

It's easy to find 60%.
Divide by 10 to find 10%,
then multiply by 6.

1 10,340 + 5,260 =

2 I think of a number. I add 54 then subtract 25. The answer is 40. What number did I first think of?

3 Add 1,580 to 6,600.

4 10,000 minus 7,800 =

5 The square of 9 =

6 Which of these numbers is a factor of 62? 29 30 31 32

7 3,600 ÷ 3 =

8 Half of 11,000 =

9 Write < or >. 395,102   539,120

10 Round 64,100 to the nearest thousand.

11 What is the next number in this sequence? 700, 660, 620, 580, ...

12 $\frac{3}{4}$ x 80 =

13 Write 0.91 as a fraction.

14 60% of 40 =

15 5 x a = 25   a =

16 If 2nd January was a Wednesday, what day was 30th December?

17 What is the perimeter of the rectangle?

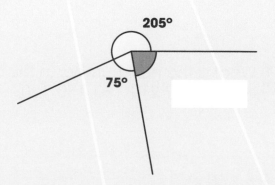

7.8cm

3.2cm

18 10km – 7,290m =

19 What size is the missing angle?

205°

75°

20 Give the mean for the following data: 11 13 15 12

Score:

1 10,470 + 4,130 =

2 I think of a number. I add 73 then subtract 27. The answer is 50. What number did I first think of?

3 Add 1,750 to 4,300.

4 10,000 minus 8,100 =

5 The square of 6 =

6 Which of these numbers is a factor of 76? 18 19 20 21

7 3,900 ÷ 3 =

8 Half of 13,000 =

9 Write < or >. 884,009   848,090

10 Round 72,500 to the nearest thousand.

11 What is the next number in this sequence? 800, 740, 680, 620, …

12 $\frac{3}{4}$ x 88 =

13 Write 0.79 as a fraction.

14 90% of 90 =

15 6 x a = 12   a =

16 If 2nd May was a Friday, what day was 30th May?

17 What is the perimeter of the rectangle?

6.2cm

4.9cm

18 10km – 6,020m =

19 What size is the missing angle?

135°

70°

20 Give the mean for the following data: 14 15 17 17

Brodie's Brain Booster

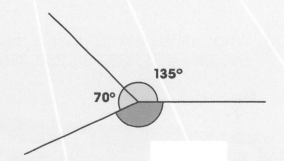

Each of Digit's dog biscuits weighs 200g. How many dog biscuits would there be if Digit's dream came true and he had a tonne of dog biscuits?

Addition, subtraction, multiplication and division

1 10,520 + 4,280 = [ ]

2 I think of a number. I add 49 then subtract 24. The answer is 60. What number did I first think of?

[ ]

3 Add 1,890 to 6,700.

4 10,000 minus 5,400 = [ ]

5 The square of 10 = [ ]

6 Which of these numbers is a factor of 92? 21 22 23 24

[ ]

7 4,200 ÷ 3 = [ ]

8 Half of 15,000 = [ ]

Number, place value and rounding

9 Write < or >. 458,250 [ ] 485,520

10 Round 89,900 to the nearest thousand.

[ ]

11 What is the next number in this sequence? 1,000, 930, 860, 790,

[ ]

Fractions, decimals and percentages

12 $\frac{3}{4}$ × 68 = [ ]

13 Write 0.43 as a fraction.

14 40% of 80 = [ ]

Algebra

15 3 × a = 21   a = [ ]

Measurement

16 If 2nd March was a Saturday, what day was 30th March?

[ ]

17 What is the perimeter of the rectangle?

[ ]

7.4cm

3.8cm

18 10km – 4,050m = [ ]

19 What size is the missing angle?

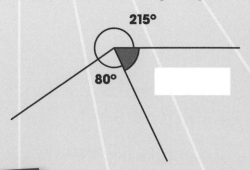

215°

80°

[ ]

Data

20 Give the mean for the following data: 19 21 17 18

[ ]

Score chart

Test	21	22	23	24	25	Progress
Score						

Score:

1 15,200 + 5,700 =

2 I think of a number. I subtract 25 then add 12. The answer is 40. What number did I think of?

3 125,000 plus 85,000 =

4 What is the difference between 12,000 and 4,800?

5 Which of these numbers is a prime number? 42 43 44 45

6 12 x 7 = 20 +

7 I think of a number. I multiply by 70 and divide by 2. The answer is 210. What number did I first think of?

8 3,600 ÷ 30 =

9 Write < or >. 275,804   257,408

10 Round 12,381 to the nearest ten thousand.

11 What is the next number in this sequence? 6,100 5,700 5,300 4,900 ...

12 $\frac{1}{4}$ x £1.60 =

13 1 - 0.63 =

14 50% of 25,000 =

15 9 x 4 = 42 - a   a =

16 A television programme starts at 5.05pm and finishes at 6.20pm. How long is the programme?

17 What is the perimeter of the triangle?

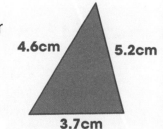

4.6cm   5.2cm   3.7cm

18 2l - 450ml =

19 What size is the missing angle?

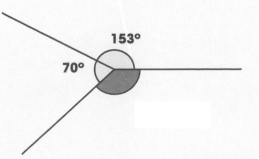

153°   70°

20 Give the mean for the following data: 8 9 6 5 7

Score:

Brodie's Brain Booster

Can you answer Digit's question: What is 6 + 4 x 3?

1 14,600 + 8,300 =

2 I think of a number. I subtract 43 then add 14. The answer is 70. What number did I first think of?

3 145,000 plus 65,000 =

4 What is the difference between 16,000 and 4,700?

5 Which of these numbers is a prime number? 51 52 53 54

6 12 x 8 = 30 +

7 I think of a number. I multiply by 90 and divide by 2. The answer is 225. What number did I first think of?

8 5,100 ÷ 30 =

9 Write < or >. 389,062 [ ] 398,026

10 Round 15,726 to the nearest ten thousand.

11 What is the next number in this sequence? 7,200 6,700 6,200 5,700 …

12 $\frac{1}{4}$ x £2.40 =

13 1 – 0.47 =

14 50% of 45,000 =

15 8 x 4 = 40 – a   a =

16 A television programme starts at 5.35pm and finishes at 6.20pm. How long is the programme?

17 What is the perimeter of the triangle?

5.6cm
2.9cr
5.4cm

18 2l – 380ml =

19 What size is the missing angle?

216°
80°

20 Give the mean for the following data: 7 4 9 6 9

Score:

1 13,500 + 9,700 =

2 I think of a number. I subtract 65 then add 17. The answer is 30. What number did I first think of?

3 175,000 plus 95,000 =

4 What is the difference between 18,000 and 6,900?

5 Which of these numbers is a prime number? 57 58 59 60

6 12 x 6 = 40 +

7 I think of a number. I multiply by 40 and divide by 2. The answer is 180. What number did I first think of?

8 4,800 ÷ 30 =

9 Write < or >. 456,100   546,001

10 Round 37,500 to the nearest ten thousand.

11 What is the next number in this sequence? 8,000 7,600 7,200 6,800 ...

12 $\frac{1}{4}$ x £3.60 =

13 1 − 0.08 =

14 50% of 75,000 =

15 12 x 4 = 60 − a   a =

16 A television programme starts at 5.55pm and finishes at 7.20pm. How long is the programme?

17 What is the perimeter of the triangle?

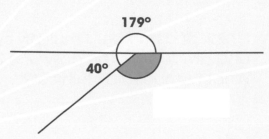

4.6cm   4.6cm

4.6cm

18 2l − 260ml =

19 What size is the missing angle?

179°

40°

20 Give the mean for the following data: 6 6 11 8 9

Digit says...

Multiplication has to be done before subtraction too. So in a question like 12 − 2 x 5 you have to do the 2 x 5 before subtracting from 12. A cat just wouldn't get that right.

Score:

1 16,300 + 7,800 =

2 I think of a number. I subtract 56 then add 18. The answer is 60. What number did I first think of?

3 155,000 plus 45,000 =

4 What is the difference between 17,000 and 5,600?

5 Which of these numbers is a prime number? 73 74 75 76

6 12 x 5 = 20 +

7 I think of a number. I multiply by 60 and divide by 2. The answer is 240. What number did I think of?

8 1,800 ÷ 30 =

9 Write < or >. 578,500 _____ 587,050

10 Round 41,860 to the nearest ten thousand.

11 What is the next number in this sequence? 9,000 8,400 7,800 7,200, …

12 $\frac{1}{4}$ x £3.20 =

13 1 – 0.81 =

14 50% of 95,000 =

15 7 x 4 = 50 – a   a =

16 A television programme starts at 5.42pm and finishes at 6.15pm. How long is the programme?

17 What is the perimeter of the triangle?

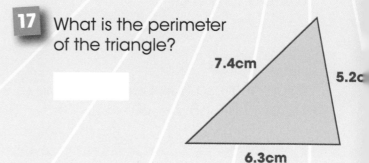

7.4cm

5.2c

6.3cm

18 2l – 720ml =

19 What size is the missing angle?

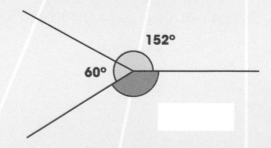

152°

60°

20 Give the mean for the following data: 12 8 7 13 15

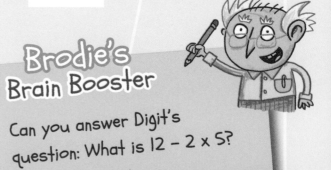

Brodie's Brain Booster

Can you answer Digit's question: What is 12 – 2 x 5?

Score:

Digit says...

Did you know that the angles inside a quadrilateral add up to 360°? Cats don't even care about angles!

1 11,800 + 9,500 =

2 I think of a number. I subtract 73 then add 19. The answer is 50. What number did I first think of?

3 165,000 plus 65,000 =

4 What is the difference between 14,000 and 7,800?

5 Which of these numbers is a prime number? 81 82 83 84

6 12 × 4 = 30 +

7 I think of a number. I multiply by 30 and divide by 2. The answer is 135. What number did I first think of?

8 2,100 ÷ 30 =

9 Write < or >. 623,297 ___ 632,279

10 Round 59,025 to the nearest ten thousand.

11 What is the next number in this sequence? 10,000 9,300 8,600 7,900 ...

12 $\frac{1}{4}$ × £4.80 =

13 1 – 0.54 =

14 50% of 83,000 =

15 6 × 4 = 40 – a   a =

16 A television programme starts at 5.38pm and finishes at 6.18pm. How long is the programme?

17 What is the perimeter of the triangle?

6.5cm   5.4cm   4.8cm

18 2l – 870ml =

19 What size is the missing angle?

164°   50°

20 Give the mean for the following data: 7 18 14 12 9

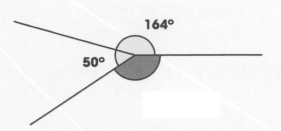

Addition, subtraction, multiplication and division

1 12,900 + 8,600 =

2 I think of a number. I subtract 86 then add 16. The answer is 40. What number did I first think of?

3 135,000 plus 95,000 =

4 What is the difference between 16,000 and 8,800?

5 Which of these numbers is a prime number? 89 90 91 92

6 12 x 9 = 70 +

7 I think of a number. I multiply by 80 and divide by 2. The answer is 280. What number did I first think of?

8 2,700 ÷ 30 =

Number, place value and rounding

9 Write < or >. 798,358 [ ] 789,385

10 Round 98,123 to the nearest ten thousand.

11 What is the next number in this sequence? 10,000 9,200 8,400 7,600 …

Fractions, decimals and percentages

12 $\frac{1}{4}$ x £5.00 =

13 1 – 0.17 =

14 50% of 47,000 =

Algebra

15 11 x 4 = 70 – a   a =

Measurement

16 A television programme starts at 5.51pm and finishes at 6.35pm. How long is the programme?

17 What is the perimeter of the triangle?

7.4cm   6.3c

5.2cm

18 2l – 960ml =

19 What size is the missing angle?

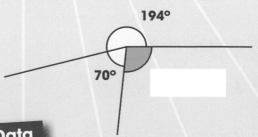

194°

70°

Data

20 Give the mean for the following data: 16 11 15 18 20

Score chart

Test	26	27	28	29	30	Progress
Score						

TEST 31

1 86,000 + 35,000 =

2 I think of a number. I add 1,400 then subtract 800. The answer is 1,200. What number did I first think of?

3 Increase 476,000 by 19,000.

4 What is my change from £10 when I spend £2.45?

5 Which of these numbers is not a multiple of 15? 75 50 45 90

6 400 x 4 = 200 x

7 I think of a number. I multiply by 16 and divide by 2. The answer is 48. What number did I first think of?

8 21,000 ÷ 3 =

9 Write < or >. 1,416,089   1,614,008

10 Round 269,164 to the nearest ten thousand.

11 What is the next number in this sequence? 12,900 12,200 11,500 10,800 …

12 $\frac{1}{4}$ of 1.2kg =

13 2.4 x 3 =

14 75% of 300 =

15 20 – a = 3 x 4   a =

16 A film is 1 hour 25 minutes long. It starts at 7.30pm. What time does it finish?

17 What is the perimeter of the pentagon?

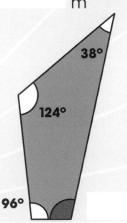

3.7cm 3.7cm 3.7cm 3.7cm 3.7cm

18 Double 2.4km =   m

19 What size is the missing angle?

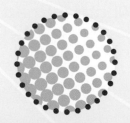

38°
124°
96°

20 Give the mean for the following data: 14 15 16 17 18

Brodie's Brain Booster

How much is 10% of 4.5kg?

Give your answer in grams.

39

Score:

1 92,000 + 43,000 =

2 I think of a number. I add 1,600 then subtract 400. The answer is 1,800. What number did I first think of?

3 Increase 569,000 by 17,000.

4 What is my change from £10 when I spend £4.78?

5 Which of these numbers is not a multiple of 12? 38 48 60 72

6 500 x 4 = 100 x

7 I think of a number. I multiply by 12 and divide by 2. The answer is 42. What number did I first think of?

8 42,000 ÷ 3 =

9 Write < or >. 1,416,089 ___ 1,614,008

10 Round 342,164 to the nearest ten thousand.

11 What is the next number in this sequence? 14,000, 13,300, 12,600, 11,900, ...

12 $\frac{1}{4}$ of 3.2kg =

13 3.2 x 4 =

14 75% of 500 =

15 30 – a = 3 x 6   a =

16 A film is 1 hour 45 minutes long. It starts at 6.30pm. What time does it finish?

17 What is the perimeter of the pentagon?

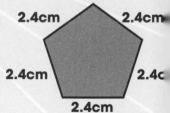

2.4cm   2.4cm
2.4cm   2.4c
2.4cm

18 Double 3.6km = ___ m

19 What size is the missing angle?

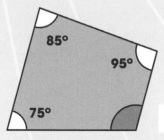

85°
95°
75°

20 Give the mean for the following data: 11 13 9 10 14

Digit says...

It's a good job that I'm kind enough to wake my human at 6.15am because he's been asleep for 435 minutes.

TEST 33

Brodie's Brain Booster

How much is 5% of 4.5kg?
Give your answer in grams.
The answer to my last Brain
Booster should help you.

1 73,000 + 38,000 =

2 I think of a number. I add 1,300 then subtract 700. The answer is 1,900. What number did I first think of?

3 Increase 258,000 by 16,000.

4 What is my change from £10 when I spend £6.56?

5 Which of these numbers is not a multiple of 13? 26 39 52 64

6 300 x 4 = 400 x

7 I think of a number. I multiply by 13 and divide by 2. The answer is 26. What number did I first think of?

8 51,000 ÷ 3 =

9 Write < or >. 7,416,089   7,146,800

10 Round 123,236 to the nearest ten thousand.

11 What is the next number in this sequence?
71,400 70,700 70,000 69,300 …

12 $\frac{1}{4}$ of 3.6kg =

13 1.7 x 5 =

14 75% of 600 =

15 40 – a = 3 x 7   a =

16 A film is 1 hour 50 minutes long. It starts at 8.30pm. At what time does it finish?

17 What is the perimeter of the pentagon?

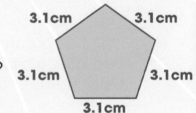

3.1cm   3.1cm   3.1cm   3.1cm   3.1cm

18 Double 4.5km =   m

19 What size is the missing angle?

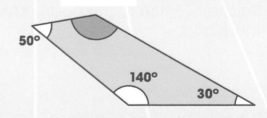

50°   140°   30°

20 Give the mean for the following data:
21 27 24 19 13

41

Score:

Digit says...

Because there are 60 seconds in every minute I know that my human sleeps for 26,100 seconds every night. What a waste of time.

1 69,000 + 57,000 =

2 I think of a number. I add 1,500 then subtract 600. The answer is 1,700. What number did I first think of?

3 Increase 625,000 by 18,000.

4 What is my change from £10 when I spend £8.63?

5 Which of these numbers is not a multiple of 14? 44 56 70 84

6 700 x 4 = 200 x

7 I think of a number. I multiply by 18 and divide by 2. The answer is 54. What number did I first think of?

8 69,000 ÷ 3 =

9 Write < or >. 8,416,089   8,461,980

10 Round 678,456 to the nearest ten thousand.

11 What is the next number in this sequence? 46,200 45,500 44,800 44,100 …

12 $\frac{1}{4}$ of 1.6kg =

13 5.9 x 6 =

14 75% of 800 =

15 20 – a = 3 x 5   a =

16 A film is 1 hour 38 minutes long. It starts at 5.30pm. what time does it finish?

17 What is the perimeter of the pentagon?

2.7cm 2.7cm 2.7cm 2.7c 2.7cm

18 Double 1.6km =   m

19 What size is the missing angle?

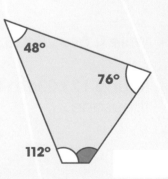

48° 76° 112°

20 Give the mean for the following data: 13 15 18 16 12

Score:

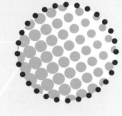

1 81,000 + 69,000 =

2 I think of a number. I add 1,700 then subtract 900. The answer is 1,800. What number did I first think of?

3 Increase 687,000 by 31,000.

4 What is my change from £10 when I spend £7.87?

5 Which of these numbers is not a multiple of 16? 16 32 48 62

6 800 x 4 = 1600 x

7 I think of a number. I multiply by 22 and divide by 2. The answer is 33. What number did I first think of?

8 78,000 ÷ 3 =

9 Write < or >. 6,416,089 ☐ 6,164,998

10 Round 567,753 to the nearest ten thousand.

11 What is the next number in this sequence? 57,500 56,700 55,900 55,100 …

12 $\frac{1}{4}$ of 2.8kg =

13 8.7 x 3 =

14 75% of 700 =

15 30 − a = 3 x 8   a =

16 A film is 1 hour 29 minutes long. It starts at 6.30pm. What time does it finish?

17 What is the perimeter of the pentagon?

3.2cm 3.2cm 3.2cm 3.2cm 3.2cm

18 Double 2.9km =   m

19 What size is the missing angle?

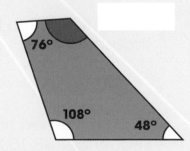

76° 108° 48°

Brodie's Brain Booster

How much is 15% of 4.5kg? Give your answer in grams. The answers to my last two Brain Boosters should help you.

20 Give the mean for the following data: 14 16 23 19 14

Addition, subtraction, multiplication and division

1 78,000 + 56,000 =

2 I think of a number. I add 1,200 then subtract 700. The answer is 1,900. What number did I firs think of?

3 Increase 579,000 by 49,000.

4 What is my change from £10 when I spend £3.59?

5 Which of these numbers is not a multiple of 15? 30 45 60 80

6 600 x 4 = 800 x

7 I think of a number. I multiply by 17 and divide by 2. The answer is 17. What number did I first think of?

8 81,000 ÷ 3 =

Number, place value and rounding

9 Write < or >. 9,416,089 [ ] 9,641,000

10 Round 456,159 to the nearest ten thousand.

11 What is the next number in this sequence? 48,100 47,200 46,300 45,400 …

Fractions, decimals and percentages

12 $\frac{1}{4}$ x 2.4kg =

13 7.4 x 7 =

14 75% of 900 =

Algebra

15 40 – a = 3 x 12   a =

Measurement

16 A film is 1 hour 43 minutes long. It starts at 7.30pm. What time does it finish?

17 What is the perimeter of the pentagon?

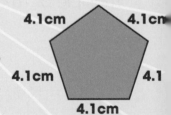

4.1cm 4.1cm 4.1cm 4.1 4.1cm

18 Double 3.8km = [ ] m

19 What size is the missing angle?

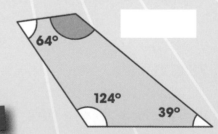

64° 124° 39°

Data

20 Give the mean for the following data: 17 15 18 24 19

Score chart

Test	31	32	33	34	35	Progress
Score						

ANSWERS

	Test 1	Test 2	Test 3	Test 4	Test 5	Progress Test 1
1	22	31	21	37	36	42
2	200	310	650	410	490	840
3	182	271	633	851	773	462
4	740	650	220	410	320	270
5	90	130	196	150	190	110
6	55	62	49	71	44	78
7	21	24	18	23	19	17
8	8.9	9.3	4.7	6.8	8.3	5.6
9	>	<	<	>	>	<
10	180	220	470	480	390	890
11	62	97	91	102	79	73
12	$\frac{1}{2}$	$\frac{1}{2}$	$\frac{1}{3}$	$\frac{1}{4}$	$\frac{1}{5}$	$\frac{3}{4}$
13	0.25	0.5	0.75	0.3	0.7	0.9
14	8	24	17	53	68	76
15	2	3	6	16	13	7
16	30	15	45	15	30	45
17	24cm²	18cm²	12cm²	20cm²	28cm²	28cm²
18	38cm	62cm	54cm	41cm	72cm	19cm
19	38°	67°	53°	44°	26°	72°
20	10	20	24	30	25	29

	Test 6	Test 7	Test 8	Test 9	Test 10	Progress Test 2
1	23	50	58	43	57	32
2	619	743	865	902	549	824
3	281	448	522	836	763	666
4	621	445	318	297	501	283
5	46	36	57	28	89	93
6	72	45	36	63	54	99
7	8	3	5	6	7	12
8	105	205	305	165	215	315
9	<	<	>	<	<	>
10	570	430	640	980	870	760
11	80	95	93	105	100	103
12	$\frac{3}{4}$	$\frac{3}{4}$	$\frac{2}{3}$	$\frac{2}{3}$	$\frac{4}{5}$	$\frac{2}{3}$
13	$\frac{1}{2}$ or $\frac{5}{10}$	$\frac{1}{4}$	$\frac{3}{4}$	$\frac{9}{10}$	$\frac{7}{10}$	$\frac{3}{10}$
14	18	14	10	12	16	15
15	6	7	4	1	3	3
16	10	20	6	5	12	50
17	10cm²	12.5cm²	15cm²	20cm²	21cm²	27cm²
18	611m	376m	421m	593m	292m	489m
19	104°	126°	97°	135°	118°	123°
20	10	15	21	15	15	25

	Test 11	Test 12	Test 13	Test 14	Test 15	Progress Test 3
1	43	37	47	62	67	57
2	3,500	5,900	6,900	8,000	5,000	5,700
3	181	335	208	112	322	237
4	42p	42p	16p	30p	39p	16p
5	36	16	25	49	64	81
6	66	19	29	37	47	58
7	425	325	225	125	175	375
8	2.3	4.7	8.1	6.9	5.2	7.7
9	>	<	>	>	<	<
10	1,040	3,220	4,150	6,000	4,110	8,230
11	66	80	50	37	69	88
12	33	42	34	44	24	24
13	2.4	3.5	1.8	4.2	2.4	4.5
14	30	50	70	90	120	180
15	3	4	11	8	7	8
16	90	75	105	150	135	165
17	$16cm^2$	$6.4cm^2$	$12cm^2$	$10.8cm^2$	$12.8cm^2$	$19.2cm^2$
18	512ml	271ml	196ml	361ml	763ml	852ml
19	70°	100°	100°	60°	50°	90°
20	10.5	20.5	19.5	17.5	18.5	22.5

	Test 16	Test 17	Test 18	Test 19	Test 20	Progress Test 4
1	2,200	2,300	2,400	2,600	2,200	2,100
2	410	611	644	643	801	929
3	1,110	1,470	1,190	1,270	4,290	5,170
4	2,550	3,550	1,350	2,620	3,090	2,430
5	8	27	64	8	27	64
6	20	12	14	0	18	30
7	16.7	23.9	35.8	92.4	70.6	11.8
8	1	7	2	3	3	4
9	<	<	>	>	>	<
10	2,700	5,100	7,900	6,300	3,600	5,000
11	79	78	60	50	33	99
12	24	12	18	17	21	23
13	0.42	0.57	0.93	0.69	0.38	0.77
14	3	4	6	10	12	28
15	11	11	5	13	13	20
16	4.15pm	6.55pm	8.05pm	7.12pm	6.10pm	5.25pm
17	18.4cm	12.8cm	29.6cm	23.6cm	11.2cm	18cm
18	2,600m	6,400m	2,600m	3,200m	2,100m	1,700m
19	73°	83°	59°	69°	65°	69°
20	9.25	7.25	5.25	8.25	7.25	10.25

	Test 21	Test 22	Test 23	Test 24	Test 25	Progress Test 5
1	14,600	16,700	17,800	15,600	14,600	14,800
2	44	14	23	11	4	35
3	5,060	6,670	6,090	8,180	6,050	8,590
4	7,400	6,300	5,400	2,200	1,900	4,600
5	49	25	16	81	36	100
6	6	13	23	31	19	23
7	800	600	900	1,200	1,300	1,400
8	2,500	3,500	4,500	5,500	6,500	7,500
9	<	>	<	<	>	<
10	15,000	23,000	38,000	64,000	73,000	90,000
11	400	520	90	540	560	720
12	36	18	45	60	66	51
13	$\frac{69}{100}$	$\frac{71}{100}$	$\frac{83}{100}$	$\frac{91}{100}$	$\frac{79}{100}$	$\frac{43}{100}$
14	28	24	42	24	81	32
15	4	9	8	5	2	7
16	Thursday	Friday	Tuesday	Sunday	Friday	Saturday
17	18.2cm	17.6cm	20.6cm	22cm	22.2cm	22.4cm
18	8,520m	6,740m	1,530m	2,710m	3,980m	5,950
19	140°	120°	140°	80°	155°	65°
20	7 75	8 75	10 75	12 75	15 75	18 75

	Test 26	Test 27	Test 28	Test 29	Test 30	Progress Test 6
1	20,900	22,900	23,200	24,100	21,300	21,500
2	53	99	78	98	104	110
3	210,000	210,000	270,000	200,000	230,000	230,000
4	7,200	11,300	11,100	11,400	6,200	7,200
5	43	53	59	73	83	89
6	64	66	32	40	18	38
7	6	5	9	8	9	7
8	120	170	160	60	70	90
9	>	<	<	<	<	>
10	10,000	20,000	40,000	40,000	60,000	100,000
11	4,500	5,200	6,400	6,600	7,200	6,800
12	40p	60p	90p	80p	£1.20	£1.25
13	0.37	0.53	0.92	0.19	0.46	0.83
14	12,500	22,500	37,500	47,500	41,500	23,500
15	6	8	12	22	16	26
16	1hour 15 mins	45 minutes	1hour 25 mins	33 minutes	40 minutes	44 minutes
17	13.5cm	13.9cm	13.8cm	18.9cm	16.7cm	18.9cm
18	1.55l	1.62l	1.74l	1.28l	1.13l	1.04l
19	137°	64°	141°	148°	146°	96°
20	7	7	8	11	12	16

	Test 31	Test 32	Test 33	Test 34	Test 35	Progress Test 7
1	121,000	135,000	111,000	126,000	150,000	134,000
2	600	600	1,300	800	1,000	1,400
3	495,000	586,000	274,000	643,000	718,000	628,000
4	£7.55	£5.22	£3.44	£1.37	£2.13	£6.41
5	50	38	64	44	62	80
6	8	20	3	14	2	3
7	6	7	4	6	3	2
8	7,000	14,000	17,000	23,000	26,000	27,000
9	<	<	>	<	>	<
10	270,000	340,000	120,000	680,000	570,000	460,000
11	10,100	11,200	68,600	43,400	54,300	44,500
12	300g	800g	900g	400g	700g	600g
13	7.2	12.8	8.5	35.4	26.1	51.8
14	225	375	450	600	525	675
15	8	12	19	5	6	4
16	8.55pm	8.15pm	10.20pm	7.08pm	7.59pm	9.13pm
17	18.5cm	12cm	15.5cm	13.5cm	16cm	20.5cm
18	4,800m	7,200	9,000	3200	5,800	7600
19	102°	105°	140°	124°	128°	133°
20	16	11.4	20.8	14.8	17.2	18.6

Brodie's Brain Booster

Test 1	12
Test 3	147
Test 5	200,000
Test 7	43
Test 9	5
Test 11	25
Test 13	£12.50
Test 15	£37.50
Test 17	£6.25
Test 19	9
Test 21	1,500g
Test 23	17,500ml
Test 25	5,000
Test 27	18
Test 29	2
Test 31	450g
Test 33	225g
Test 35	675g

Digit says...

"Well done! Great job!"

DK Eye Wonder

Bugs

LONDON, NEW YORK, MUNICH,
MELBOURNE, and DELHI

Written and edited by Penelope York
Designed by Janet Allis

Managing editor Sue Leonard
Managing art editor Rachael Foster
Jacket design Chris Drew
Picture researcher Jo Haddon
Production Kate Oliver
DTP designer Almudena Díaz
Consultant Paul Pearce-Kelly

First published in Great Britain in 2002 by
Dorling Kindersley Limited
80 Strand, London WC2R 0RL

4 6 8 10 9 7 5 3

A Penguin Company
Copyright © 2002 Dorling Kindersley Limited
First paperback edition 2005

Paperback edition ISBN-13: 978-1-4053-0879-3
ISBN-10: 1-4053-0879-6
Hardback edition ISBN-13: 978-0-7513-2930-8
ISBN-10: 0-7513-2930-4
Colour reproduction by Colourscan, Singapore
Printed and bound in Italy by L.E.G.O.

see our complete
catalogue at
www.dk.com

Contents

Bugs, bugs, bugs

Most of the bugs that you know are called arthropods, which means they have their skeleton on the outside of their bodies. There are over a million known species of arthropods on the Earth. Here are a few types to spot.

We know that insects were around over 40 million years ago because some were trapped in a substance called amber, which hardened back then.

Thorax

Head

Abdomen

What is an insect?

You can spot an insect by counting its body parts and legs. They all have six legs and three body parts – a head, a thorax, and an abdomen.

Extreme bugs

• The petroleum fly lives in puddles of crude oil and feeds on insects that get stuck in it.

• Some midges can be put into boiling water and survive.

• Snow fleas can survive in sub-zero temperatures. If you pick one up it will die in the heat of your hand.

What is a myriapod?

If you try counting the legs on a creepy crawly and you find you can't, the chances are you are looking at a myriapod, such as a millipede or centipede. They have lots of segments and lots and lots of legs!

What is an arachnid?

All arachnids have eight legs. Watch out however, other than spiders, a lot of arachnids look like insects so count carefully.

What is a true bug?

These days we tend to call all creepy crawlies "bugs" – as we have in this book. But actually a true bug is a type of insect that has a long mouthpart that it pierces its food with, then uses it to suck up the inside of the food.

Leapers and creepers

Some bugs are speedy, some are slow. Some bugs run and others jump. They all have their reasons why they do what they do and a lot depends on where they live – different obstacles demand different types of movement.

High jump
The flea is the most powerful jumper of all insects. It has a little spring in its legs to enable it to jump very high. It can jump 600 times an hour for three days, when it is looking for a host.

Legging it
The green tiger beetle is
the fastest insect on earth.
It runs at 1 m (3 1/2 ft) per
second. It uses its speed to catch
other insects and to run quickly
across the hot desert sand.

Leaps and bounds
If a grasshopper or cricket is
disturbed and it needs to get
away, it uses its massively
developed, muscle-
packed legs to leap
high into the air.

A grasshopper can leap 20 times the length of its body

Looping upwards
Some caterpillars loop their way
up branches. They attach their
back leg suckers to the branch
and stretch their bodies forwards,
then loop up their back, pulling
the suckers upwards. They can
walk up some pretty steep twigs.

Keeping in step
A millipede has up to 180 pairs of legs!
They all help it force its way through the
soil. It has to be very co-ordinated when
it walks otherwise its legs bump into
each other. It moves them in waves.

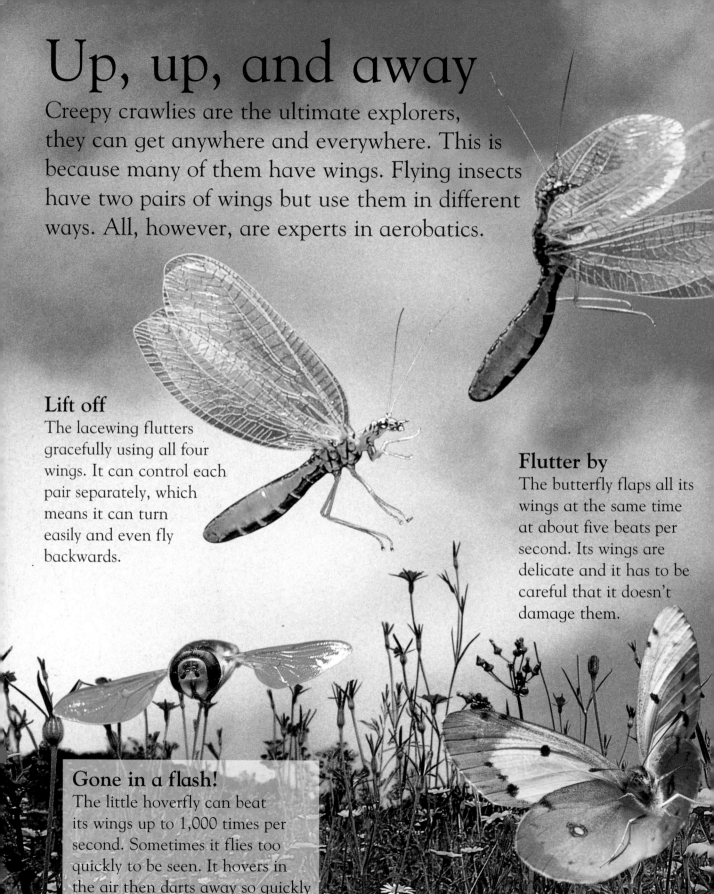

Up, up, and away

Creepy crawlies are the ultimate explorers, they can get anywhere and everywhere. This is because many of them have wings. Flying insects have two pairs of wings but use them in different ways. All, however, are experts in aerobatics.

Lift off
The lacewing flutters gracefully using all four wings. It can control each pair separately, which means it can turn easily and even fly backwards.

Flutter by
The butterfly flaps all its wings at the same time at about five beats per second. Its wings are delicate and it has to be careful that it doesn't damage them.

Gone in a flash!
The little hoverfly can beat its wings up to 1,000 times per second. Sometimes it flies too quickly to be seen. It hovers in the air then darts away so quickly that it seems to disappear.

Haltere

Cruise control

The second set of wings on flies have turned into halteres that look like drumsticks. The fly uses these for balance and co-ordination and they help the fly to change direction in a split second.

A hard case

The beetle only uses one pair of wings to fly with. Their front wings have become hard cases that protect the flying wings when they are folded away.

THE INCREDIBLE JOURNEY

When the winter cold sets in, in the Rocky Mountains, North America, the monarch butterfly migrates up to 3,000 miles to the finer weather in California and Mexico. This insect covers 80 miles a day and travels in huge groups. They always settle on the same tree as the year before, at the end of their journey, and no-one knows how they find their way.

Making sense

Imagine being able to taste with your feet, or having eyes as big as your head. Sounds odd? Well bugs have some pretty strange ways to find their way around and sniff each other out.

Feeling the way

Some insects, such as this cave cricket, live in dark places where there is little light. Because of this their eyesight is not good. Instead they use long feelers, or "antennae", which stop them from bumping into walls all the time in the pitch black.

Powerful perfume

Antennae are also used to smell. This male moth has two hairy antennae that can smell a female moth from 11 km ($6^1/2$ miles) away!

A matter of taste

This butterfly tastes with its feet. When it lands on a particularly tasty flower, its long mouthparts, or "proboscis", unfold automatically and allow it to drink.

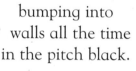

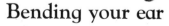

Bending your ear

Bug's ears can be found on their wings, bellies, or heads and believe it or not, this katydid (bush cricket) listens with its knees! The slits on the legs are ears that can pick up other cricket's calls.

Bug-eyed
The horsefly's enormous eyes take up almost all of its head. Its eyes are very sensitive to movement, which is why it is so incredibly difficult to swat.

Meat eaters

There are so many bugs around, you would have thought it would be easy for predators to catch and eat them. Wrong, hunters have to invent cunning ways to get their dinner, and have weird ways to eat it too.

The waiting game

A praying mantis hides camouflaged among leaves where it sits still for a very long time with its forelegs ready to strike. When an insect passes, it pounces at lightning speed and chews it up in its jaws.

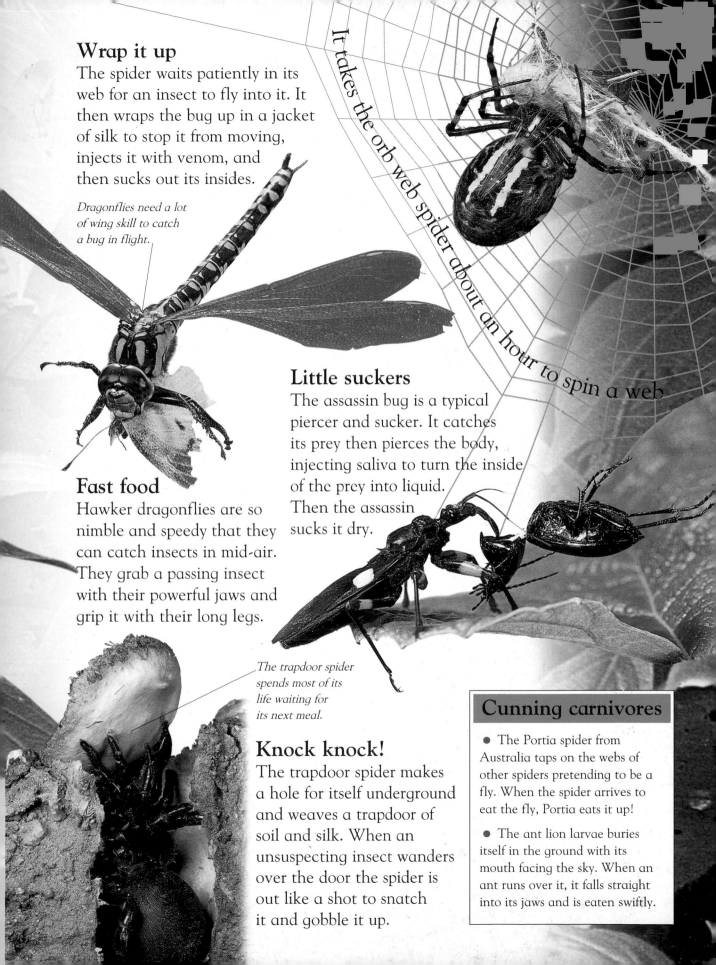

Wrap it up

The spider waits patiently in its web for an insect to fly into it. It then wraps the bug up in a jacket of silk to stop it from moving, injects it with venom, and then sucks out its insides.

Dragonflies need a lot of wing skill to catch a bug in flight.

It takes the orb web spider about an hour to spin a web

Fast food

Hawker dragonflies are so nimble and speedy that they can catch insects in mid-air. They grab a passing insect with their powerful jaws and grip it with their long legs.

Little suckers

The assassin bug is a typical piercer and sucker. It catches its prey then pierces the body, injecting saliva to turn the inside of the prey into liquid. Then the assassin sucks it dry.

The trapdoor spider spends most of its life waiting for its next meal.

Knock knock!

The trapdoor spider makes a hole for itself underground and weaves a trapdoor of soil and silk. When an unsuspecting insect wanders over the door the spider is out like a shot to snatch it and gobble it up.

Cunning carnivores

● The Portia spider from Australia taps on the webs of other spiders pretending to be a fly. When the spider arrives to eat the fly, Portia eats it up!

● The ant lion larvae buries itself in the ground with its mouth facing the sky. When an ant runs over it, it falls straight into its jaws and is eaten swiftly.

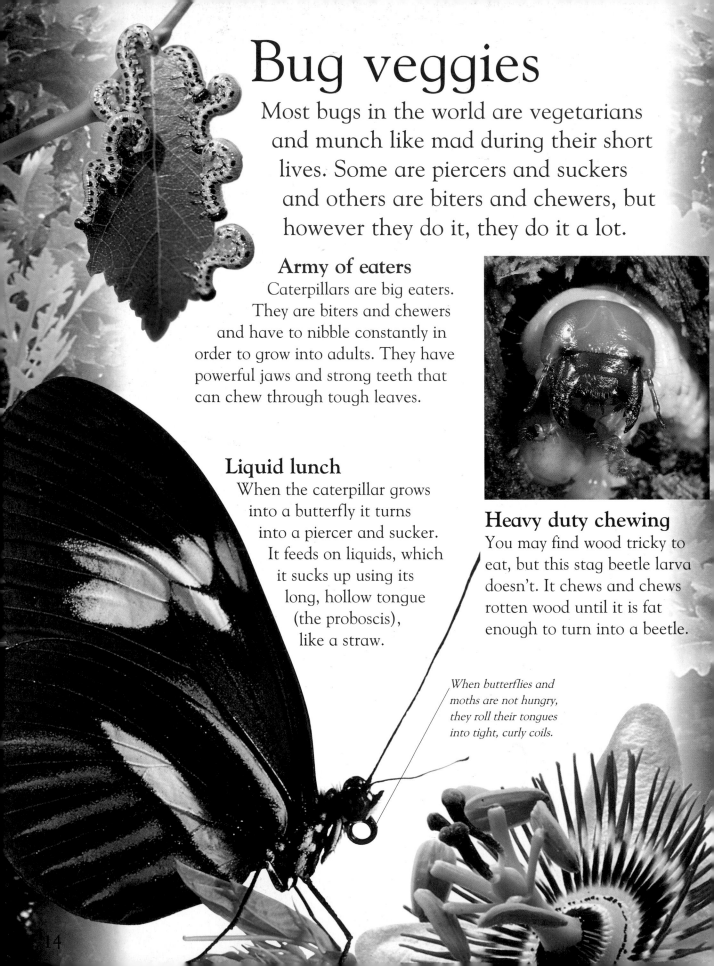

Bug veggies

Most bugs in the world are vegetarians and munch like mad during their short lives. Some are piercers and suckers and others are biters and chewers, but however they do it, they do it a lot.

Army of eaters

Caterpillars are big eaters. They are biters and chewers and have to nibble constantly in order to grow into adults. They have powerful jaws and strong teeth that can chew through tough leaves.

Liquid lunch

When the caterpillar grows into a butterfly it turns into a piercer and sucker. It feeds on liquids, which it sucks up using its long, hollow tongue (the proboscis), like a straw.

Heavy duty chewing

You may find wood tricky to eat, but this stag beetle larva doesn't. It chews and chews rotten wood until it is fat enough to turn into a beetle.

When butterflies and moths are not hungry, they roll their tongues into tight, curly coils.

Nuts about nuts

The acorn weevil only eats acorns and is an unusual eater. It pierces the hard nut with its long snout, and chomps away inside with the jaws it has at the end of it. It then sucks the food up the snout into its body.

This weevil also lays its eggs in acorns

Now you see me...

Lurking in the undergrowth there are many bugs that look like bugs, and many bugs that don't. Cunning camouflages help some bugs to catch a meal and others to avoid becoming one.

Spiky survivors

Birds are not going to risk landing on a prickly branch, so what better a disguise than to look like a spiky thorn – as long as these treehopper bugs keep still.

Flower power

If you look carefully at these beautiful flowers, you will be able to work out the shape of an orchid mantis. It can change colour from white to pink to blend in with the particular flower that it chooses to sit on.

Lost among leaves

As long as this leaf mimic katydid sticks to the right leaves, it definitely won't be spotted. It even has veins on its back just like the real leaves have.

Dropping in

Yuk, that bird dropping doesn't look very good to eat. Wrong – it's actually a very tasty king swallowtail butterfly caterpillar.

Twiggy

At first glance it is just an innocent looking twig. Look again. This walking stick insect makes sure he doesn't come to a sticky end.

MOTH STORY

Once in England there lived a pale coloured peppered moth that hid against the light coloured bark on trees. By the late 19th century the moths mysteriously started to become darker. Eventually it was realized this was because the pollution from the factories had darkened the trees. Only the darker moths remained camouflaged and they were the only ones that survived.

Playing dead

Look closely at these dead leaves – one of them is very much alive. The cryptic moth sits on the decaying leaf and is almost invisible. No-one is going to spot it there.

Warning signals

Some bugs make it obvious to their attackers that they would be nasty to eat. They make it known in various ways "Don't eat me or you'll be sorry". Others have methods that startle hunters, and a few use clever disguises.

Snake scare

It may look like a snake, but it's actually a caterpillar! This crafty creature is safe from hunters. Who would risk eating a snake?

Making eyes

Imagine taking a quick glance at this little banana eater butterfly. You'd think that those eyes were on a much bigger and more ferocious beast.

Hot bomb

A bombardier beetle under attack has a deadly revenge. It squirts a chemical out of its bottom at high speed and at a temperature of nearly 100°C!

Ultimate defence

When attacked, the puss moth caterpillar rears up its colourful head. Bright colours warn a predator that a bug is poisonous so they leave it alone.

Weta whack

Disturb the enormous weta cricket and you are in for a shock. Quick as a flash it shoots its back legs up to give a sharp kick.

Odd one out

Some bugs are lazy. They are not poisonous so they copy the colours of something that is, so they are left alone. Can you tell the difference between the bee with a sting and the harmless hoverfly? No? Good disguise! The bee is on the left.

Mother care

Most creepy crawlies lay their eggs and abandon them to fend for themselves. Others make sure that the eggs will hatch on their first meal, and a few make very good mums indeed.

Doomed!

The parasitic wasp lays its eggs on a live caterpillar, which can't shake them off. The caterpillar carries on getting fatter and juicier until the eggs hatch out and gobble him up. A yummy first meal!

Born alive

The aphid is a weird breeder. It gives birth to live young – unusual for an insect – and doesn't even need to mate with a male to give birth. If they all survived, one aphid could produce billions more in six months. Luckily lots of bugs eat the aphids or we would be over-run!

Protective shield

The mother shieldbug looks after her young with great care. Sometimes she glues them to the male's back for him to look after until they hatch! When they are born she guards them fiercely.

An aphid being born.

Piggyback ride

The jungle scorpion is a very good mum. She gives birth to live young, catching them as they are born, and pops them onto her back for two weeks until they are strong enough to fend for themselves. She can carry up to 30 babies at a time.

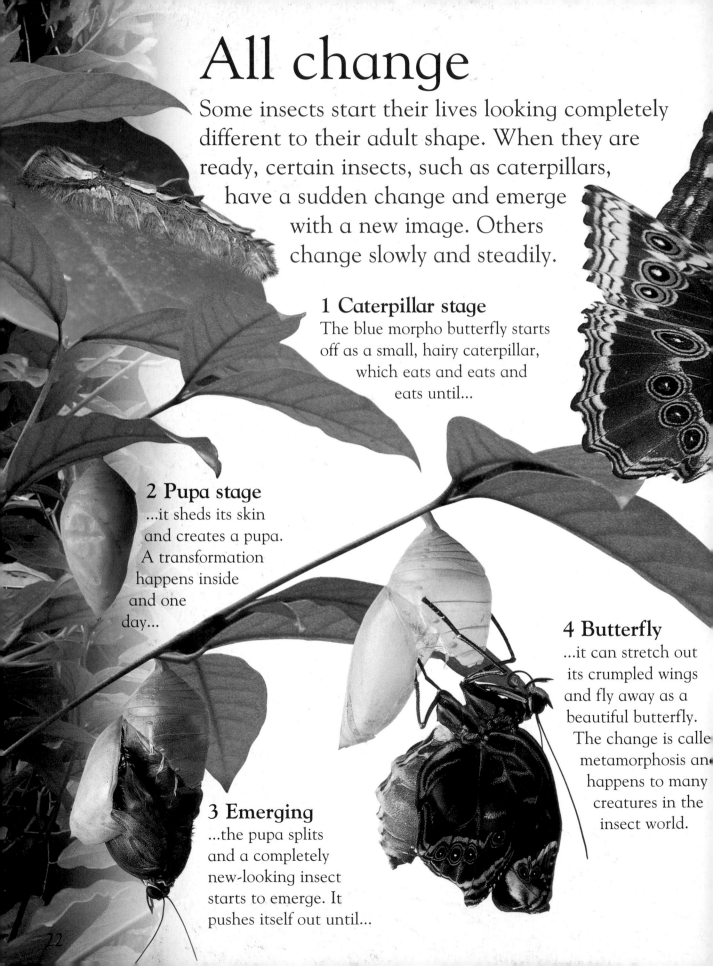

All change

Some insects start their lives looking completely different to their adult shape. When they are ready, certain insects, such as caterpillars, have a sudden change and emerge with a new image. Others change slowly and steadily.

1 Caterpillar stage

The blue morpho butterfly starts off as a small, hairy caterpillar, which eats and eats and eats until...

2 Pupa stage

...it sheds its skin and creates a pupa. A transformation happens inside and one day...

4 Butterfly

...it can stretch out its crumpled wings and fly away as a beautiful butterfly. The change is calle metamorphosis an happens to many creatures in the insect world.

3 Emerging

...the pupa splits and a completely new-looking insect starts to emerge. It pushes itself out until...

Skin shedding

Some insects change slowly as they grow up, such as this dragonfly. Because insects have their skeletons, which can't grow, on the outside of their bodies, it means that they have to replace their skins in order to grow bigger. This dragonfly is shedding its skin for the last time.

Buzzing around

If you hear a buzzing sound in your garden, the chances are you are listening to something that stings, such as a bee or a wasp. But there's more to these buzzing bugs than meets the eye. They build some incredible homes and are excellent team players.

Collecting nectar

During the spring and summer, the honeybees fly from flower to flower to collect nectar. Back in the hive the nectar is used to make honey.

A hive of activity

Honeybees live in hives. Inside the hive they make a honeycomb, which is made out of wax from their glands. The six-sided cells that make up the honeycomb hold honey and the eggs, which the queen bee lays.

Bee dance

When a worker bee finds a good nectar supply, it returns back home to the hive and does a little "figure of eight" dance, which lets the other bees know where the nectar is.

Sweet tooth

Wasps love sugar and especially sweet fruits, which is why they buzz around your food in the summer, annoying you. They won't sting you, however, unless you threaten them.

Building a nest

Some wasps live in large nests made of paper. The queen wasp starts the nest by chewing dead wood, mixing it with saliva, and letting it dry. She then lays some eggs, which hatch, and the next generation carry on with the nest-building.

25

Army of helpers

Ants and termites each live in huge colonies where they build their homes together, work together, and never have time for play. Their whole life revolves around bringing up their young safely.

Loyal subjects

The queen termite is a huge, ugly egg-laying machine that never moves from her royal chamber. The termites rally around her, feeding and cleaning her.

Termite high-rise

Some species of termite live in huge mounds that they build using earth, saliva, and their droppings. The mounds can be up to 6 m (20 ft) high.

The king termite lives with the queen in her nest

Big bully

The toughest ant around is the Australian bulldog ant. It grips its meal in its huge, powerful jaws then swings its body around and stings the prey from behind. Bugs that get in his way don't stand a chance!

Firm friends

Ants and aphids are very good at keeping each other happy. The aphids eat a lot of tree sap and give off a sweet liquid that the ants like to sip. In return the ants guard them fiercely from predators.

Lots of bugs like to eat aphids, so having ant bodyguards is the best way for them to survive.

THE ANT CLEANING SERVICE

Every so often villagers in Africa receive visits from a march of up to 22 million driver ants, which forces them out of their homes. Although each ant is only 1 cm ($1/3$ in) long and blind, they kill every pest that gets in their way, such as locusts and scorpions. The villagers welcome the clean up!

Team work

Some ants build their nests by weaving together groups of leaves. They each carry a live ant larva in their jaws and make it produce silk, which they then use to sew up the leaves. If anyone threatens the nest, they attack by biting.

Deep in the jungle

Nobody knows how many species of bugs there
are in the jungle. New ones are being found
all the time, which means that there are
a lot more to be discovered. The ones
that we do know, however, are pretty odd.

Big head
The lantern fly gets its name
from its very long head,
which sticks out of its body
and has a bright end on it.
Some lantern flies (which
are actually bugs, not flies)
are huge, with a wingspan
of up to 15 cm (6 in).

Giant of the jungle
The giant tiger centipede is very
large and aggressive. It runs at
high speeds across the forest floor,
using its many legs. It eats other
bugs and sometimes even toads,
lizards, or small mammals.

Queen of flight
The Queen Alexandra's birdwing is the largest butterfly in the world, and one of the rarest. It's wingspan can grow to 28 cm (11 in).

Spiny postman
The postman butterfly caterpillar has sharp spikes all over its soft body, which protect it from predators. It feeds on poisonous passion flower leaves that are absorbed into its body and make it poisonous too.

Hairy, scary spider
During the day, the red-kneed tarantula sleeps in its silk-lined burrow. Then, when it starts to get dark, it emerges for the night hunt searching for large insects and injecting them with venom.

Sand devils

The desert is a tough place to live. Not many plants grow there and there is little water around. Bugs need to be pretty clever if they are going to survive one of the hottest places on earth.

Living larders

The honeypot ant workers feed other honeypot ants with lots of nectar, which they store in their huge tummies. When food is short, the ants with the pot-bellies vomit up the honey that they have made and feed it to the workers.

Jewel of the desert

The jewel wasp is solitary – it doesn't live in a swarm. Here it is stinging a cockroach that it will lay its egg on. A first tasty meal for its youngster.

The store ants spend all their lives hanging from the ceiling

Best pals
Without each other, the yucca moth and the yucca plant wouldn't survive. The moth lays her eggs on the plant and in return pollinates it as she does so. The newborn caterpillars eat the seeds, but leave enough for new plants to grow.

Dew drinker
The darkling beetle has a clever way to find its drink. It waits until the morning when dew has formed on its back, then leans forward and catches it as it trickles into its mouth.

A sting in the tail
This desert scorpion hardly ever needs to drink. It gets most of its moisture from the spiders and insects that it eats. Its sting is so poisonous that it could kill a person.

Desert carpet
Large swarms of these desert locusts eat in the cool of the night and rest during the day's heat. Sometimes, there are so many that they look like a huge desert carpet.

Water world

If you find a body of water, the chances are it's filled with mini-life – but you may have to look closely to see some of it. Many bugs live in or above the water and some can even walk on the surface.

Diving in
The diving beetle is the great meat eater of the water. It tucks a bubble of air under its wings so it can breathe underwater, and dives down to catch tadpoles and even small fish.

Walking on water

Pond skaters can walk on water because of thick, waterproof hairs on their feet. They skim over the surface looking for floating food.

Darting around

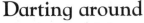

The beautiful dragonfly lives above water. It is called the dragonfly because of its very aggressive "dragon-like" behaviour.

Bottoms up!

Mosquito larvae live in the water. When they need air, they swim to the surface and hang there with their snorkel-like breathing tubes poking up through the top.

Back stroke

The water boatman hangs upside down just beneath the surface. It looks like a little boat and its back legs are just like oars, which is how it got its name.

Caddis armour

The larva of the caddis fly builds a case around itself to protect it. It makes the case out of stones, shells, and pieces of plants.

Watery web

The air-breathing water spider makes a diving bell to live in. It weaves a web under water, among the plants, and stocks it with air from the surface.

Little mites

This house dust mite is 0.3mm (0.001 in) long and eats flakes of your dead skin. You have millions of dust mites in your home, which live in mattresses, furnishings, and carpets. They can cause people to sneeze and wheeze.

House mites

You may try to forget that bugs live all over your home, but the fact is they are there. They may not all be nasty, but they have one thing in common – they like living with us.

Spiders in the home

The house spider likes to hide in dark places in your home, such as down a plug hole. Sometimes you will spot it scuttling across the floor to eat flies and other bugs.

What a louse!

Once a female head louse has a tight grip on one of your hairs, she is very difficult to get rid of. She can lay 50 eggs (nits), each at the base of a single hair. She causes your head to itch because she sucks blood from your scalp.

Fly alert!

Flies love to share the food you eat. They vomit their digestive juices on to your meal, which turns it into liquid that they suck up into their bodies.

Unwanted guests

Cockroaches are badly behaved visitors. They eat anything tasty they can find in the home and once settled are very difficult to get rid of.

As dusk falls...

As day turns into night, some insects are just starting to wake up. Whether they are avoiding being eaten, or getting ready for a meal, night is a pretty lively time in bug land.

Moon moth
The first time it flies, the Indian moon moth takes to the air after dark to avoid being eaten. It doesn't have a mouth because it only lives long enough to survive on the food it ate when it was a caterpillar.

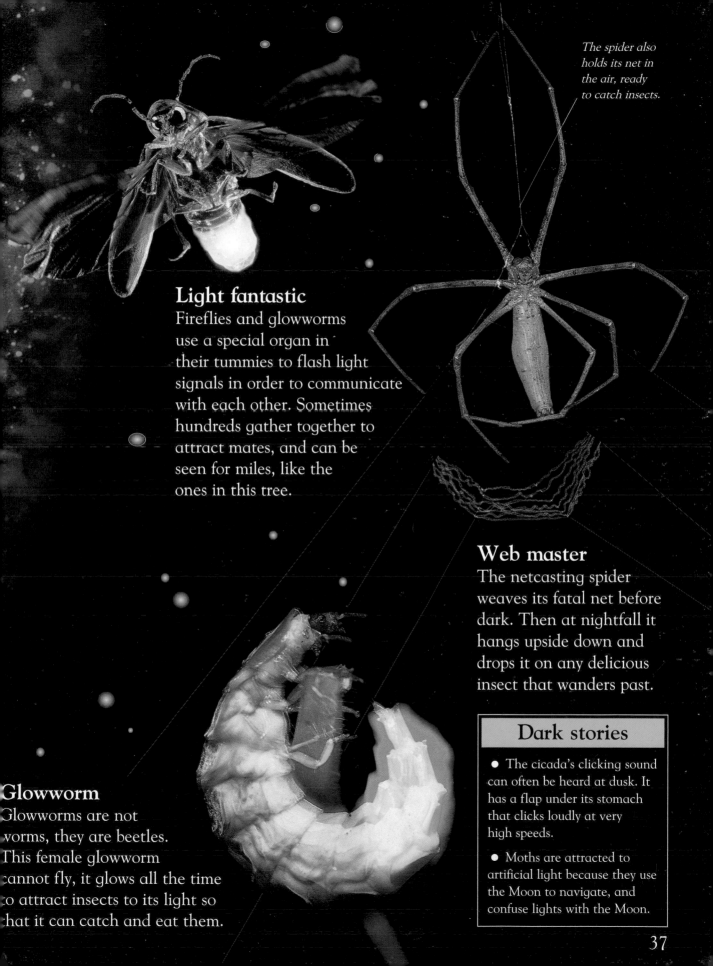

The spider also holds its net in the air, ready to catch insects.

Light fantastic

Fireflies and glowworms use a special organ in their tummies to flash light signals in order to communicate with each other. Sometimes hundreds gather together to attract mates, and can be seen for miles, like the ones in this tree.

Web master

The netcasting spider weaves its fatal net before dark. Then at nightfall it hangs upside down and drops it on any delicious insect that wanders past.

Glowworm

Glowworms are not worms, they are beetles. This female glowworm cannot fly, it glows all the time to attract insects to its light so that it can catch and eat them.

Dark stories

● The cicada's clicking sound can often be heard at dusk. It has a flap under its stomach that clicks loudly at very high speeds.

● Moths are attracted to artificial light because they use the Moon to navigate, and confuse lights with the Moon.

Weird and wonderful

There are so many bugs that have evolved mysterious habits and strange looks that they could fill a whole book. Here is a small selection from around the world.

How weird would it be to have eyes on the end of stalks?

Eyes on stalks

The eyes of stalk-eyed flies are on the top of long stalks. When two males meet they compare eyes and the one with the widest set gets the girl.

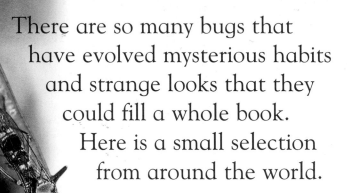

Terrifying taste

The flambeau butterfly has very strange taste in food. It sits on an alligator's eyes and sips its tears. What a very brave little bug.

Stick your neck out

Why does the giraffe weevil have such a long neck? No-one knows. But it certainly makes it one of the weirdest looking bugs.

Mystical mantis

You can barely tell which way around this mantis is facing. If you look carefully, however, you can just see its head on the right hand side. Its strange colouring helps it to camouflage itself.

Out of this world
If you came across this katydid (a type of bush cricket) in the jungle, you'd be forgiven for thinking that we'd just been invaded by aliens, with its spiny body and strange colours.

Pests and plagues

They may be small but bugs can do a surprising amount of damage — in large numbers or on their own. Us humans sometimes have to try hard to control them, and very often we lose.

Leaping locusts

Imagine a swarm of a thousand million locusts. Yuck! A swarm this big, which we call a plague, can eat every crop in a region in a matter of hours. When there are so many locusts together at once, they blot out the Sun as they pass overhead.

Colorado killer

In 1850, settlers arrived in the mountains of North America and they brought with them the potato. These tiny Colorado beetles got a taste for potatoes and swept across America eating the lot. They are still a serious pest.

Deadly mozzy

The deadly mosquito is the world's most dangerous animal. It can spread a disease called malaria when it sucks blood, and has been responsible for killing more humans than any other living creature.

Only female mosquitos drink blood.

It's all in the kiss

The kissing bug likes to suck blood from near a human's mouth. It leaves its droppings near the bite, which can get scratched into the skin, resulting in an illness called Chagas' disease.

Big sucker

This tsetse fly is filled with blood that it has just sucked out of a human. But not only does it leave an itch, it can also leave behind a deadly disease called sleeping sickness.

A DEADLY TALE

In the past, when someone old was dying, their relatives sat up with them all night to watch them. Often the sitters would hear an eerie tap, tap, tap coming from the wooden walls. It was a small beetle that eats through timber. When it hatches from its egg it bangs its head against the wood to attract another beetle to it, making a tapping sound. That's how it got its name – the deathwatch beetle.

Cleaning up

Nature has its own recyling service in the form of bugs that feed on dead plants, animals, and dung. Left uneaten, the remains would build up into a huge pile of rotten gunge. We should be very thankful for these small cleaners!

Feeding frenzy

Maggots are the specialists on eating decaying flesh. Flies lay their eggs on rotting animals. The eggs hatch into maggots. Their stream-lined shape helps them to bury into the flesh to eat it.

Great balls of dung

When a pile of dung appears in Africa, the dung beetles rush in, each one claiming a piece of the action. The male rolls a perfect ball of dung and rolls it away and buries it. The female lays a single egg in the ball and when it hatches, the beetle grub eats the dung.

Cleaning agents

Millipedes live in damp, dark areas and are very useful cleaners. They eat any rotting leaves and dead bugs lying around, breaking them down to become part of the soil again.

DUNG DISPOSAL

When Europeans arrived in Australia, they brought cows with them (there were none there already). The dung beetles in Australia were used to dry kangaroo pellets, not the soft cowpats, and the pile of cowpats got larger and the flies got worse until an answer had to be found. So the Europeans introduced African dung beetles to Australia who were used to soft dung. The Australians now enjoy a fast rate of disposal.

The essential bug

Whether you like them or not, bugs are an essential part of our lives. We spend a lot of time trying to get rid of them but we could not live without them.

Lick it cricket
About 500 types of insect provide a good, healthy snack for people around the world. These crickets give these lollypops a nice crunch to look forward to.

Honey bee
Without bees helping to pollinate by moving pollen from flower to flower, we wouldn't have nearly as many plants as we do. Bees also supply us with endless amounts of sweet honey.

Silky threads
Did you know that when you wear silk you are actually wearing material made by a caterpillar? When the silk moth caterpillar pupates, it makes a silk lining for its pupa, which we use to weave into cloth.